The Big Pot

Kasia Reay

Illustrated by Amy Willcox

Schofield & Sims

Mi<u>ss</u> Ro<u>ss</u> has a big pot.

Fin has a big sa<u>ck</u>.

Ca<u>ss</u> and Fin tip the sa<u>ck</u> up.

Lin and Te<u>ss</u> fi<u>ll</u> the pot up.

Ca<u>ss</u> and Fin tip the can up.

Lin and Te<u>ss</u> pi<u>ck</u> the me<u>ss</u> up.

The big pot and us!